WILMETTE PUBLIC LIBRARY

D0331877

Michael Tippett

The
Midsummer Marriage

An Opera in three Acts

Libretto

ED 10778-11
ISMN M-2201-0493-0

WITHDRAWN
Wilmette Public Library

WILMETTE PUBLIC LIBRARY
1242 WILMETTE AVENUE
WILMETTE, IL 60091
847-256-5025

www.schott-music.com

Mainz · London · Madrid · New York · Paris · Prag · Tokyo · Toronto
© 1954 SCHOTT & Co. Ltd., London · Printed in Germany

NOTÆ

When fully lighted the stage, as seen from the audience, presents a clearing in a wood, perhaps at the top of a hill, against the sky. At the back of the stage is an architectural group of buildings, a kind of sanctuary, whose centre appears to be an ancient Greek temple. The stage in front of the temple and within the whole semi-circular group of buildings is raised, with steps leading down to the lower level of the main stage. To the right, as one faces the temple, these steps end in an ascending spiral stone staircase, which seems to break abruptly in mid-air. (The staircase is at the same time the last of the group of buildings to the right.) To the left, the steps lead further down through gates into the hillside itself, for the gates look like the entrance to a cave. (Like the staircase to the right, the gates and cave might be considered the left end of the group of buildings, for the cave is equally within, or at least on the edge of the sanctuary. But visually the ascending staircase is a bit nearer the temple than the descending cave.) While the sky-line is clear behind the temple, the trees of the wood seem almost to mix with the other buildings, and are plentiful (in the wings) on the lower stage as well.

As explained more clearly in the text, in Act II the scene has taken a turn to the right.

The time is the present. The costumes are of the present day, except for those of the Ancients and Dancers, which are old Greek.

DRAMATIS PERSONÆ

Mark	a young man of unknown parentage	*Tenor*
Jenifer	his betrothed, a young girl	*Soprano*
King Fisher	Jenifer's father, a business man	*Baritone*
Bella	King Fisher's secretary	*Soprano*
Jack	Bella's boy-friend, a mechanic	*Tenor*
Sosostris	a clairvoyante	*Alto*
The Ancients	Priest and Priestess of the Temple	*—Bass* *—Mezzo-Soprano*
Chorus of Mark's and Jenifer's friends		S.A.T.B.
Dancers attendant on the Ancients		Silent
Strephon	one of the dancers	Silent

ACT ONE

(*Morning*)

Scene 1. CHORUS

(The scene is in twilight before day-break.)

Semi-Chorus 1 (*off left*)
   This way! This way!
   Don't go too far down there
   But keep the path together.
      (repeated nearer)
        (Semi-Chorus 1 *enter, left)*

Men   Here's a clearing in the wood.
     Is this the place he meant ?

Girls   I hope it gets lighter soon
     Anything might happen here.
     What's that ?

Men   Only mist.
     It will clear when the sun rises.
     But where are all the rest ?

Semi-Chorus 2 (*off, right*)
   Hulloa! Hulloa!

Semi-Chorus 1 (*All*)
   That must be them calling.

Semi-Chorus 2 (*nearer*) Hulloa!

Semi-Chorus 1   Hulloa!

Semi-Chorus 2   Hulloa!

Semi-Chorus 1   We've found the place.
        Come on. Come on.

Semi-Chorus 2 (*enter right*)
   Thank heaven we've found you.

Girls (*Semi-Chorus* 2) Whatever did we come for ?

Men (*Semi-Chorus* 2) Where's Mark ?

Girls (*Semi-Chorus* 2)   Where's Jenifer?

Full Chorus: *Men*   Are you sure we've found the place?

Full Chorus: *Girls*   Oh, anything might happen here.

Men   But look, it's nearly sunrise
And getting lighter.
>   (*The scene has been getting lighter.   The sun rises.*)

All   Ah! the sun, the sun, midsummer morning!
Our spirits rise towards the bright
Comfort of the morning light.
Ah! the sun, the sun, midsummer morning.
>   (*The mist rises from the buildings*)

Girls   Oh look—the temple there!

Men   The meeting place that Mark appointed.

Girls   It seems much nearer than expected.
>   (*They look at the buildings for a moment in silence.*
>   *Strange music off ; flutes and bells*)

Girls   What's that?

Men   Surely music?

Girls   I don't like it.

Men   Listen, listen.
>   (*They listen.   Music off, again*)

Girls   Oh, I'm frightened.

Men   Don't be frightened.

Girls   Someone's coming.

Men   Let's hide away among the trees.

Girls   Yes, let's hide away among the trees.

All   Let's hide away among the trees.
>   (*They do so.*)

Scene 2. ANCIENTS, DANCERS, later MARK

(*The dancers come from the temple led by Strephon playing a flute, followed by the Ancients. A March. On a signal from the He-Ancients the dancers execute a sword [or stick] dance. A Dance. The dance end, with a clap of hands or sticks. Mark enters quickly.*)

Mark   Stop!
(*The Ancients pay no attention and order the dance a second time. Mark, after a moment's uncertainty, breaks up the dance.*)

Mark   Stop! Stop! Stop!

He-Ancient   Young man, young man,
What right have you thus to break the dance?

Mark   I want a new dance for my wedding day.
Strange was my birth
And strange my fate,
My wedding should be strange.
Is that not right?

He-Ancient   Take care! A new dance
May well be strange but dangerous.

Mark   What nonsense!

She-Ancient What impertinence!

Mark (*turning to the She-A.*)
Look at your dancers then—
They are young like me.
                    (*To the dancers*)
You want a new dance?

She-Ancient Children, be still!

He-Ancient Change the unchanging ritual,
There'll be no point of rest—

She-Ancient —No grace, no beauty.

Mark	Your words are vapours in the summer sun. On this day, this day Anything can happen And everyone shall dance for me.
He-Ancient	Then watch your new dance, And you will see. (*The He-Ancient orders the dance to begin again. Mark shows at first bewilderment and then exasperation that the dance is the same as before, until the He-Ancient, who has been moving around the dancers, suddenly trips Strephon, who falls to the ground with a crash.*)
Mark	Monstrous! Monstrous!

(Mark runs to Strephon)

Strephon, are you hurt?

(helps him up)

Can you walk?
(*Strephon tries to walk with Mark's help, and is received by the other dancers. Mark turns to the He-Ancient.*)

Mark (*passionately*)
O what a wicked thing to do,
Trying to break Strephon's leg.
Have you no sense of the proper care
For a dancer's trained body?

He-Ancient That is a lesson for *you* to learn,
Who think that change is only harmless—

She-Ancient While it may sweep all trace of fragile
Beauty from its senseless path.

Mark You twist my meaning, for you're envious of our
youth.

He-Ancient No!
We do not desire your youth, nor seek
To hold you longer from your dreams.
You shall learn a new dance
Before you leave this place today.
(*The Ancients and the Dancers return within the temple and the doors close behind them. March repeated.*)

Scene 3. MARK, CHORUS

Chorus (*coming from behind the trees*)
        Oh Mark, who are they?
        Have you known them long?

Mark   I don't know who they really are,
        But I've seen them since boyhood.

        I've come here on summer nights
        And mornings such as these.
        Then is the temple nearer.
        They are close, and if I wait
        Eventually appear.

        I call them the Ancients,
        For they're so old, and never change.
        I think they know the secret of my birth,
        But will not tell me.

        They'll come back, so let them be,
        And turn to other things:
        My marriage and my plan
        To give the ring to Jenifer
        Here in this magic wood
        And on midsummer-day.
        If no new dance,
        At least new song to greet her.
        For what can match the splendour of my pride
        When she appears before you all as my bride?

        Ah, ah . . . the summer morning dances in my
                heart.
        There, there's the lark ascending from the field.
           No man is happier than I,
           No woman lovelier than she,
        And like the lark I'll sing because I love—
           I love, I love, I love, I love—
        And like the lark I'll sing for joy because I love.
             (*Jenifer enters. She is dressed for a journey.*)

Scene 4. MARK, JENIFER, CHORUS

Mark	Jenifer, Jenifer, my darling. But—but—your dress? Upon our wedding day?
Jenifer	Today there'll be no wedding.
Mark	No wedding! Why?
Jenifer	Why? Why have I come here, Here when all the world's to choose? This heat . . . this place . . . No, no—I must go further, Out of sound and out of sight.
Mark (echoing)	Out of sight? I see. You're frightened Of your ranting father.
Jenifer	I've come away from him, And left his home for good.
Mark	And hoping for a better home You've come away to me, to me.
Jenifer	No. I must leave you too. I'll come back—perhaps—perhaps.
Mark	Jenifer, what, then don't you love me any more?
Chorus (sotto voce)	They're quarrelling. Oh, what's the trouble?
Jenifer	It isn't love I want, but truth.
Mark	Truth ? See, see—the summer morning dances in my heart.
Jenifer	It isn't love I want, but truth.
Mark	Come now, kiss me and forget!
Jenifer	Don't touch me!
Mark	Are you mad?
Jenifer	Rudeness will not hold me either. How can I break free from you all? *(turning away upstage)* Where? Where?

Chorus	They're quarrelling. Oh, what's the trouble?
	(Mark runs round in front of her)
Mark	Stop! You shan't go! I won't let you.
Jenifer	Out of my way! Out of my way! *(She walks by him and finds herself at the foot of the* *stone steps)* Now I know where I shall go. *(turning downstage)* What steps are those?
Mark (*sotto voce*)	Those steps are broken.
Jenifer	This summer sun makes me see further. *(Jenifer shades her eyes to look)*
Mark	Surely you won't ascend them ? Jenifer, for pity's sake, Don't go there.
Jenifer (*with resolution*)	For me the light! For you, the shadow! O magic staircase that I've always known In dreams since childhood at my mother's knee, At last, at last, I set my feet Upon the way to heaven. Up, up I climb to paradise. *(She slowly climbs the stone steps)*
Girls	Up, up she climbs to paradise.
Men	The staircase has no end, she's bound to fall.
Mark (*to the men*) (*to Jenifer*)	She's mad, she's mad. Come back, Jenifer, Come back. Ah— *(Jenifer unexpectedly disappears from sight)*
Mark	She's vanished in the light And I am left in darkness.
Men	Come, Mark, don't grieve. She'll come back.
Girls (*laughing*)	Ha, ha, ha, etc.

Mark	Oh, I am left in darkness.
Girls	Ha, ha, ha, etc.
King Fisher (*off right*)	Hulloa! Hulloa!
Girls	King Fisher's voice!
Men	Now, Mark, you can't stay here.
Mark	—in darkness.
King Fisher	Hulloa! Hulloa!
Girls	He's surely coming after Jenifer.
Mark	—in darkness.
Girls (*to the men*)	Oh make Mark go away!

Men   Mark, wake up! wake up!
             Up, up, up!   (*lifting him*)

Mark   —in darkness.

Men   Up, up, up!
Mark   Then let me go
             To darkness as she told me.   (*with resolution*)
             For her the light!
             For me the shadow!

             Gates I have always longed to enter,
             Open to receive your child.

(*The gates fly open. Mark enters the cave and the gates crash to behind him. King Fisher rushes on in time to see them shut and Mark disappearing.*)

Scene 5. KING FISHER, BELLA, CHORUS, ANCIENTS

Men (*laughing*) Ho, ho, ho, ho, etc.

King Fisher (*turning to the men*)
　　　　　What are you laughing at?
　　　　　It's no laughing matter
　　　　　If my daughter left me for a bastard.
　　　　　　　　　　(*after a moment he calls—*)
　　　　　Bella,—Bella,—hurry here.
　　　　　Hurry, hurry, hurry.

Bella (*off*)　Here I am.
　　　　　Here . . . (*she enters*) . . . I am.
　　　　　　　　　　(*a little breathless*)
　　　　　I was coming as quick as I could.

King Fisher　I've just seen Mark run away down there.

Bella　　　Down there?

King Fisher　Jenifer is surely with him too.

Bella　　　You think she may be with him too.

King Fisher (*looks around*)
　　　　　What sort of place is this, d'you think?

Bella　　　It's rather odd for a house.
　　　(*to the chorus*)　Does anybody live here?

Girls　　　Very strange folk indeed.

Men　　　By name the Ancients.

Girls (*ironic*)　Their door is further up.

King Fisher (*pompous*)
　　　　　Knock then, Bella, and enquire within.
　　　　　　　　(*Bella goes on to the upper stage*)

Bella　　　There's no knocker, but a kind of bell.

　　　　　　　　　(*She rings a hanging bell*)

(*After a moment's expectation, the doors of the temple slowly open, and the Ancients come gravely through them and on to the upper stage.　King Fisher goes downstage R. and keeps his back turned to the Ancients.*)

She-Ancient Who are you?
What do you want?

Bella (*matter-of-fact and quickly*)
I'm King Fisher's secretary.
He wants me to ask you about those gates.
He thinks his daughter may be down there.
Do you know if that is so?

She-Ancient Where his daughter goes is her affair.

He-Ancient The gates are strange,
And only open for the proper people.
(*Bella goes downstage to where King Fisher is, and reports—*)

Bella They say the gates are strange,
And open only for the proper people.

King Fisher What riddling is that?
I fear they're not worth talking to
But ask them who the proper people are.
(*Bella returns to the Ancients*)

Bella (*with pride*) The great King Fisher wants to know—

She-Ancient (*interrupting*)
Should he not speak to us himself?
He's easily in hearing.

Bella (*outraged*) That would never do.
He deals with everyone through me.
He only speaks, speaks
To people as important as himself.

He-Ancient Tell him there are no proper people here.
(*Bella goes again to King Fisher, and reports—*

Bella They say the proper people are not here.

King Fisher What rigmarole! Tell them
I need the gates set open or I'll force them.

Bella I don't think they'll consent to that.

King Fisher Then we'll proceed without consent. (*dismisses her*)

(*Bella turns to go. The Ancients have returned into the
temple.*)

Bella	Oh! They're gone! How very odd.
King Fisher (*turning round*)	
	That's no behaviour fit for me. I'll not forget.—And now?
Bella	Perhaps you'll have to force the gates, Though they will certainly object.
King Fisher	Who's to do that?
Bella	Well, there's Jack.
King Fisher	Who's Jack ?
Bella	Oh—he's a honey.
King Fisher	A what?
Bella	I mean a workman—a mechanic.
King Fisher	Then Jack's the man for me. Go. Go. Fetch him at once.
Bella	But—
King Fisher	Go. Go. No more delay. Go. (*Bella goes.*) I'll keep watch till you return.

Scene 6. KING FISHER, CHORUS

King Fisher (*turning to the men*)
So you, so you—are Mark's fine brood of friends.
But he's a ne'er-do-well, a ne'er-do-well,
A loafer sponging on the state,
Whom you presume to emulate
This summer morning.

Do not be misled, my boys,
Mark's a tempter and a rascal,
Stealing your hearts away from work
And duty you so gladly shirk
This summer morning.

While I, King Fisher, I, the clever business man,
Trying by all the means I know
To guard the honour of my daughter,
I've some work for you.   (*pointing left*)
To spy that way behind that wall,
To see the dangers to expect.
What! You shy away.
Where's your sense of courage and adventure?
Will that not spur you? Will that not spur you?
Then I'll call the tune.
You fancy people may despise me,
But look—here's money!
                    (*He takes a purse from his pocket.*)
Don't you like it?
                    (*He holds up a coin and waves it before them.*)
Don't you want it?
Here! Catch, catch.   Catch, catch.
Catch if you can
                    (*He throws the coin to the men.*)

Chorus (*Men*) Here! Catch, catch.   Catch, catch.
Catch if you can.

King Fisher (*interrupting*)
Now, you boys, it's time to start
To do the work you're paid for,
So let me see you go.
That way! That way!

The sooner the going
The quicker return,
The quicker return,
And remember, you fellows, remember,
Don't dally around,
Swimming in streams
So gay in the sun there
High in the heavens
Already at noon,
For I am the boss now,
And pay for you.

(*King Fisher drives the men off left, and turns to the girls.*)

So you, so you—so you're the company my
daughter keeps.
But she's her head in air, her head in air,
In cloud cuckoo-land,—'twas child's play
For Mark to make her run away
This summer morning.

Do not be beguiled my dears
For I, King Fisher, I, a loving, generous father,
Hoping to show you, if I can,
The real way to help my daughter,
I've some work for you   (*pointing right*)
To spy that way behind the wall
To see what dangers to expect.
What!   You shy away.
Where's your sense of pity and compassion?
Will not that move you?   Will not that move you?
You fancy people may despise me,
But look—here's money!

(*He takes a purse again from his pocket.*)
Don't you like it?
Don't you want it?

(*He takes out a coin as before and prepares to throw it to the girls, but before he can do so they recoil.*)

Chorus (*Girls*)	No! No!
King Fisher	What?
Chorus (*Girls*)	No!
King Fisher	What?
Chorus (*Girls*)	No! Whatever you offer, No truck with a bribe, No truck with a bribe.
King Fisher (*furious*)	Are you crack-pots, Or very high-minded, Refusing a wage

Paid for the work
That's got to be done?
Well, boggle at money,
You'll do it without,
For I am the King here.
Be off with you!
    (*He drives the girls off, right, and is left alone.*)

Scene 7. KING FISHER, JACK, BELLA, later CHORUS

(Enter Bella with Jack.   He is in overalls.)

Jack Here I am, Sir,
What can I do?

King Fisher I want the gates there opened.
Do it promptly.   I'll pay you well.
(Jack goes to try the gates.)

Jack They're firmly shut.   But sure
We'll have them open in a moment.
(He comes back to look in his bag for a tool.)

Bella Should we not ask the owners if they mind?

King Fisher No!
You spoke with them yourself and know it's
useless.
(Jack goes to try the gates again.)

Bella But *do* be careful, Jack, you know
I'm worried by the people here.

Jack But even if you are,
What can I do?

King Fisher Take no notice!   No.

Jack No.

King Fisher and Jack
A job's a job, and there's no question,
A working man must do as told,
And trust the one who pays him, for
A job's a job and there's no question.

(Jack prepares the tools he is to use.)

Jack Like ev'ry working man I know
How best to do my single job.
My card'll tell you who I am
And what the weekly wage I earn.
But it can't tell you what I dream.

Bella   Ah, Jack!

Jack   That's only known to *me*—

Bella   Ah, Jack!

Jack   To *me*—and you.

Bella   Ah!

Bella and Jack   Ah, ah,
Life's dull until our work is over,
When you and I walk out together,
Down the roadway courting, for
Life's dull until our work is over.
> (*They dance and embrace.*)

King Fisher (*interrupting*)
Just come along, you two, and hurry.
Your working hours aren't over yet.

Jack   Very well then, I'll begin.
> (*He lifts a hammer to do so.*)

Voice of Sosostris (*apparently from within the gates*)
Take care,
King Fisher.
A well-wisher
Says: Beware!

Bella (*anxiously*)   Whatever's that?
I knew for certain
They'd be offended.

Chorus (*Girls*) (*offstage*)
Stop!
Stop, stop!
Stop, stop!   (*They enter right.*)
Stop, O stop, King Fisher now
We know it's wrong to tamper with the gates.
Stop, we implore you!
Stop, we implore you!
Tell Jack, your man who's standing by them now,
To stop!

Bella   There, Jack, you see
They think as I do—as I do.

Jack   But, Bella, they're merely frightened by a voice,
               frightened by a voice.

Bella   No, Jack, no, they think as I do etc. . . .

King Fisher (*shouting*)   Quiet! Quiet!
               Be quiet all of you, don't babble.
               Nothing's there to be afraid of.
               Go on, Jack, go on, Jack,
               I'll answer for you.

Jack   Very well, I'll try again. (*He does so.*)

Voice of Sosostris (*apparently from within the gates*)
               Take great care,
               Proud King Fisher.
               A true well-wisher
               Says again; Beware!

Bella   The warning voice again.
               Oh dear, it's certain
               They've been offended.

Girls   Ah . . .

Men (*offstage*)   On!
               On, On!
               On, On!   (*They enter left.*)
               On, go on, King Fisher, now
               We know the voice is nothing but a trick.
               Go on, we advise you,
               Go on, we advise you.
               Make Jack, your man, who's standing by the gates
               Go on.

Jack   There, Bella, there,
               What did I tell you?

Bella   Don't listen to them, Jack. etc. . . .
               They're quite mistaken.

Jack   But, Bella, but Bella
               Surely they're saying what they know?
               But surely you're being frightened by a voice
               That's all a trick.

Bella   Don't listen to them, Jack,
                 They're quite mistaken,
                 But *they*, they think as I do, etc.

Girls   Stop, O stop etc. . . .

Men   Go on, go on we exhort you
                 Make Jack, your man, who's standing by the gates
                 Go on.

King Fisher (*shouting*)
                 O but my patience is exhausted.
                 What do you take me for, a fool?
                 There'll be no further stalling at the labour you've
                         undertaken.

                 So: (*storming*)
                 Go on, go on, for I'm your master.

Bella   Dear Jack, I'm frightened now.
                 Do leave it.

King Fisher   Go on, for I'm your master.

Jack   Then I've no choice,
                 But I don't like it.

Chorus (*Men*)   *We* know it's but a game to trick us
                      In hopes to see us go.

Chorus (*Girls*)   *We* know he'd better leave the gates
                      that shut the path to hell.

Bella (*To Jack*)   Why must all this rest on you
                      To make so terrible a move?

King Fisher (*to Jack*)
                 Why be so frightened by a voice
                 While I am there to stand beside you?

Men   Jack should pay no further heed to Bella's
                             womanish misgivings, etc.

Girls   Jack won't pay sufficient heed to Bella's
                             sibylline misgivings, etc.

Bella	Dear Jack, I'm frightened now. Do leave it in some other hands than yours.
King Fisher	Go on, go on, for I'm your master Who intends a duty to be done.
Men	Will King Fisher be deterred by a mere voice Within the gates? Shake the whole earth with the sound of our shout Go on!
Girls	Then where can we now turn for aid In this extremity of apprehension? Lift up your voice to the heavens, and cry: Help!
Men	Shake the whole earth with the sound of our shout: Go on!
Girls	Lift up your voice to the heavens, and cry: Help!
King Fisher	Hear your master who commands you to obey. Hear your master who commands you to proceed
Bella	Trust your sweetheart who sees clearly. Trust your sweetheart who knows best.

Scene 8. Finale

KING FISHER, CHORUS, JENIFER, later MARK, ANCIENTS, DANCERS

(*Jenifer appears at the top of the steps, in white, partially transfigured.* *)
(*Jack and Bella slip away.*)

Girls   Jenifer!

Men   Jenifer!

King Fisher My daughter, Jenifer!

Jenifer (*she slowly descends to the bottom.*)
     Returning to the earth is cruel.
     Here you are never still nor calm.

King Fisher Don't give yourself such airs, young lady.
     It's a wonder you are not with Mark.

Jenifer   A very gracious heavenly wonder
     That makes him infinitely far away.

King Fisher He's safely far away down there.
     So surely now's the proper time
     To leave him?
     Come now with me
     And drop this childish masquerade.

Jenifer   Am I not masked before my earthly father?
     Now is too late to run from Mark.
     My return makes him return.

     (*The gates open. Mark appears in the gates' mouth in red,
     partially transfigured.† He shades his eyes against the light
     and stands thus for some time.*)

---

 * The ancient Greek prototype towards which Jenifer's transfiguration is tending would be Athena. (Athena was born without mother from Zeus' head). No exact imitation of Athena is meant, for the natural Jenifer is still visible behind the supernatural transformation.

 † The ancient Greek prototype towards which Mark's transfigurasion is tending would be Dionysus. (Dionysus, son of earth-born Semele, had a second birth from Zeus' thigh.) No exact imitation of Dionysus is meant, for the natural Mark is still visible behind the super-natural transformation.

Mark   Returning to the light is cruel.
Here you are ever calm and dull.
(*passionately*)
Beats not my body to the wine-red blood?

Jenifer   Flies not my spirit to the swan-white sky?
Singing: I am a child of the starry heaven.

Mark   Shouting: I am a child of the fruitful earth.

Jenifer   —of the starry heaven.

Mark   —of the fruitful earth.

Jenifer   —of heaven.

Mark   —of earth.

Jenifer   —of heaven.

Mark   —of
(*Fanfare. The temple doors open and the
Ancients come out with the Dancers.*)

He-Ancient Prepare to justify your strife.
Let the girl speak first.

She-Ancient (*coming forward between Mark and Jenifer*)
See no hint of spiritual pride
Mar the contest that you now begin.
Pride has subtle and peculiar power
To swell the stomach but not heal the heart.
You are contained within the spirit,
Not the spirit shrunk in you,
Else it burst the bonds and break you.
(*She returns upstage. The girl dancers have
now taken position near Jenifer.*)

Jenifer   Is it so strange if I resent
The fatal pressure from the world around me
Denying life to my poor straitened soul?

For her sake, then, with clear intent
Leaving the home, I thrust my lover from me,
To climb the staircase to my heavenly goal.
(*A girl dancer climbs the steps behind
Jenifer to blow upon a silver trumpet.*)
Sweet was the peace,
Joyful the calm,

Strong was the light,
Cleansing the air.
(*The girl dancers move to the music.*)
Then the congregation of the stars began
To dance: while I in pure delight
Saw how my soul flowered at the sight
And leaving the body forward ran
To dance as well.   How can I
Such lovely visions of the mind deny?
(*The girls of the Chorus begin to move with
the dancers and try to get nearer Jenifer.*)

Girls   Teach us, Jenifer, to rise
Above our cares into the skies.

King Fisher (*interrupting, and trying to reach Jenifer through the girls and
the girl dancers.*)
We live on earth and not in heaven,
Nor is there disgrace in that.
Common folk have common cares
And common duties to their state.
So—

He-Ancient (*interrupting*)
All comment is clearly out of place
While judgment is suspended for the half.
Therefore stand back!   It is the other's turn.
(*The men dancers have taken position near Mark,
driving King Fisher once more down-stage.*)

Mark (*to the Men of the Chorus*)
You, you who were with me when she left me,
How did the lover look when she had gone?

Men   A crestfallen cock,
A crumpled child
Crying: darkness.

Mark   Then when you had lifted me against my will
What outer darkness answered to my own?

Men   A deeper dark
Disclosed abruptly
In the hill-side hidden.

Mark   When I passed the gate of horn
What happened then, reading the riddle right?

Men   How could we see behind the bars
      No summer sunshine following in?

        (A man dancer ascends the hillside behind Mark
          to clash later a pair of bronze cymbals.)

Mark   Down, downwards to the centre,
      Doubled downwards,
      Crawling, falling,
      Rocked in a boat across the water
      Coldly lapping
      The waste land
      To thread the labyrinthine maze
      Of fear that guards the lovely meadows.

Men   That is no song to rouse our tired
      Hearts and steel our lazy limbs.

      (The cymbals clash. The men dancers move to the music.)

Mark   As stallions stamping
      The young men dance
      To the springing sap
      And the leaping life.
      We force our feet through the great grass
      And tear the boughs from the bending trees
      That hold the sun from the glorious bed
      Where she, lying fallow through the winter.
      Slept, till pricked awake by our desire.

Men *(beginning to be fascinated by the singing and the dancing)*
      This music rises as the spring tides
      Rise to overflow before they ebb.

Mark   As stallions stamping
      The young men dance
      To the springing sap
      And the leaping life.

      The ewe is torn by our willing hands,
      The child trod by our frenzied feet
      That beat the beat of life inflamed
      By death. There is no union but in full
      Communion, Man with Beast and All in One.

      (The men of the Chorus begin to move with the
        dancers, and try to get nearer to Mark.)

Men   Show us, Mark, another birth
As common children of the earth.

Jenifer (*taking a step forward*)
Ah, but the price for that, the price?

Men   The price?

Jenifer   See by a heavenly magic in this glass
The fearful face behind the mask.
                (She moves slowly and triumphantly
                        across the stage towards Mark.)
Look as I bring it near you, look,
Mark, that you may see the truth.
Are you so easy shamed to turn aside?
        (exultant)
Ah, what a triumph for the right!

Mark   Did I not learn a magic too
From all that happened in the cave?
Here I take this golden branch
Whose vital virtue now lets me
Turn in power. Jenifer,
Prepare to see your mirror—fall.

        (He turns and the glass falls from Jenifer's hands.)

Jenifer   Oh—what an evil devil's stroke!
Malefic magic and perverted power.
Are you a serpent, I become a saint?
Then am I Mark, and go to find the beast.

(She enters the gates, her dress catching the reflection of a red glow. The gates close behind her. During the next music, Mark crosses to the steps and slowly climbs them, his dress catching the reflection of a white light. He goes out of sight. The Ancients and dancers go into the temple.)

King Fisher Now is this nonsense at its noon.
But I'll be even with it yet.
                     (to the girls)
Jenifer has lost her senses utterly
Possessed by this midsummer madness.

Chorus (*Girls*)   Joan heard the voice first
In father's garden at high noon,
The summer sun prefiguring the flame.

King Fisher (*to the Men*)
Mark shall go down and fetch her back,
And then, perhaps, I'll give him leave to marry.

Chorus (*Men*)   Mark has no ear for you, King Fisher,
Climbing his path from hell to heaven.
No promise, nor the threat
Of violence will hold him now.

King Fisher   But mark my words, the insulting boy
Will come to heel and whimper in the end.
(*He goes off, as the Chorus join together
and wheel down to the front of the stage.*)

Chorus (*full*) Let Mark and Jenifer endure for us
The perils of the royal way.
We are the laughing children.
(*They laugh.*)

We are the laughing children.
Free, fresh, fine,
Strong, straight, stark,
Rough, raw, rude,
Gallant, grim and gay.

CURTAIN

ACT TWO

(*Afternoon*)

(*The stage set is turned slightly to the right, so that the stone steps have gone out of sight and only the doors and the left-hand corner of the temple are visible, slantwise across the right of the stage. The gates are now left-centre with more of the wood and hillside in view to the further left.*)

Pre-Scene. STREPHON, CHORUS off stage

(*Strephon is discovered standing motionless on the corner of the temple steps, listening. After a while, Strephon relaxes his pose and begins to dance down centre. He stops, hesitates, then runs off behind the temple, as the Chorus are heard singing in the distance. The Chorus' song comes nearer.*)

Chorus (*off-stage*)

> In the summer season on the longest day of all
> We wander through the woods where the cunning
>   cuckoos call,
> Crying as they're flying and this is what they say:
> She must leap and he must fall
> When the bright sun shines on midsummer-day.

Scene 1. BELLA, JACK, SEMI-CHORUS

(*Full Chorus off stage*)

(*Bella enters left, with Jack behind her. A section of the Chorus follows. The rest of the Chorus continue on their way, moving off stage from left to right, and singing their song repeatedly.*)

Bella (*drawing Jack down stage away from the Semi-Chorus*)

> Jack, don't let's go with all the others,
> Stay behind a bit with me.
> I've something for your ear alone.

Semi-Chorus (*Girls*)
> Where are you two going?
> Aren't you coming with us to play games?

Semi-Chorus (*Men*)
> Perhaps they've games of their own to play!
>   (*They all laugh.*)

Girls   Let them go or we shall lose the others.
>   (*They turn to go.*)

Men	That's true.
Chorus (all)	Bye, bye.
	In the summer season on the longest day of all . . .
	etc.

(They go back off stage after the others.
Their voices disappear too into the distance.)

Jack	They've gone now, Bella.
	What is for my ear alone?
Bella	I think you ought to guess.
	That shouldn't be so hard.
Jack	I know you've always something new in mind.
	But I can never guess.
Bella	Oh! This time is quite different.
	What day is it?
Jack	Midsummer-day.
Bella	Isn't that excuse enough?
Jack (*with good humoured patience*)	
	I've no idea.
Bella	Oh! Jack, Jack!
	Is it leap year?
Jack (*less patiently*)	
	You know the answer, Bella.
	Why ask me?
Bella	I feel as though it should be.
	For Jack, you see, I've made my mind up.
	It's time we married.
Jack	But Bella, I thought you—
Bella (*interrupting*)	
	Ah, that's past and gone.
	We're going to marry now and settle.
	Aren't you pleased?
Jack	Indeed I am!
	Only the first shock of your decision.
	So many problems rush to mind.
Bella	Which you, the handyman, will solve.
	While I, so far, have only one thing clear.
	We're going to marry, settle down and have a home.
	Agreed?

Jack	Agreed.
Bella	If there's a little house to rent, A girl can live her proper life.
Jack	A man in love was never meant To wait for ever for his wife.
Bella	And so as girl—
Jack	—and man
Bella	We come—
Jack	—together—
Bella	—in our home.
Both	And then—
Bella	While you're at work I'll mind the place And wash the clothes and cook the food
Jack	And I'll work overtime in case We need more money in the purse.
Bella	For soon—
Jack	—there'll be
Bella	A little Jack—
Jack	—or little Bella
Bella	Who can tell?
Both	And then—
Bella	I'll lay the baby to my breast And rock it, rock it gently in my arms: Sleep, sleep, pretty little one, sleep.
Jack	And when the baby's quiet I'll lift you on to my knee And rock you, rock you to Sleep, Sleep, pretty little one, sleep.
Both	Sleep, sleep, pretty little one, sleep. *(They kiss.)*

Bella	Come within the shadow of the wood.
	      *(They get up and begin to move slowly across
	        the stage. They stop and kiss again.)*

Jack	We'll go within the shadow of the wood.
	      *(They walk together slowly as in a dream
	        across the stage into the wood left.)*

Scene 2.   STREPHON, DANCERS

Strephon enters from behind the temple. He goes to the corner of the temple steps, and takes up there the same pose as in the pre-scene. Once again after a while he relaxes his pose and begins to dance lightly down stage. Strephon ends his dance down stage centre in an attitude of expectation, to the music of bells and flutes. Some of the trees appear to move. They move again. It is the other dancers who, breaking loose from their tree shapes begin to move freely about the stage. Strephon goes offstage behind the temple.

The remaining dancers gaily mark the first racing course, for the first dance, with themselves as trees. The course is a roughly circular field with trees on the perimeter and one in the centre. When the course is set, the fact is announced by a flourish. The dancers stiffen into the roots of great trees, whose branches seem to disappear into the flies.
The Hare (Strephon) enters from the right on the upper stage beside the temple, and takes his place there, crouching at the root of one of the trees. At the same time, the Hound (the girl dancer) enters, down on the lower stage, and takes her place there, waiting.

The First Dance—The Earth in Autumn

The Hound begins to hunt the Hare by scent, moving across the front of the stage from left to right. The Hound, getting warmer on the scent, begins to mount the steps to the upper stage. Here, at last, she gets the full scent, but is uncertain of the direction.

The Hare suddenly flies off, descending to the lower stage, and begins to run the course anti-clockwise, starting up stage. He moves in and out of the trees on the perimeter. The Hound chases after the Hare, but still mainly by scent. Twice the Hare is nearly caught, but on the third occasion when it looks as if capture were inevitable, the Hare does a double turn round the central tree, escapes, and runs off right. Here he is for a moment jubilant before going off the upper stage behind the temple.

In a dazzle of sunlight, the dancers come loose from the tree roots, and the trees themselves disappear. The Hound has gone off left.

The dancers move about again freely. They begin to mark the second course, for the second dance, always with themselves as trees. The course is a river, with trees on the banks, flowing diagonally across the stage down from the place where the temple steps end, right centre, to the left footlights. As before, the completion of the operation is marked by a flourish. The dancers stiffen into the roots of trees as before.

The Fish (Strephon) enters from the right on the upper stage, but near the footlights. He slides into his place, at the top of the river, sheltered by a tree root. At the same time, the Otter (a girl dancer) enters from the left upstage, and takes her place on the bank of the river, opposite the Fish.

The Second Dance—The Waters in Winter

The river begins to flow. The flow is visible where, down stage left, the water seems to eddy in the sunlight. The eddies have the form of water nymphs.

The Fish suddenly makes for the surface of the river to breathe, or catch flies. His direction is downstage. The Otter dives into the river. The Fish flashes back to the safety of the bank, sheltering under a tree root further down the river on the same side. The Otter swims about and whips up the waters in her anger. She climbs out of the river opposite the Fish. The commotion subsides. The eddies become noticeable again in the sunlight.

Once more, the Fish darts, and the Otter plunges after him. The Fish regains the bank further down on the same side, but the Otter climbs out on the same side of the river as the Fish, though further down. The commotion subsides once more. The eddies are visible again, but the air is troubled.

The fish makes a dash, attempting to get past the Otter, who dives after him, pinning him against the further bank. The Fish gets entangled with the water numphs, seeking to force himself through crannies too small for the Otter to pass. He seems to get stuck in one, and only escapes with a wrench. He goes off right onto the upper stage, but this time his jubilation is marred by the pain due to the wrench. He goes offstage right behind the temple.

In a dazzle of sunlight the dancers get loose from the tree roots and the river disappears. The Otter has gone off stage left.

The dancers sow a field of spring corn, moving right across the stage and returning. They begin to dance in ever smaller circles, gradually spinning into a group which finally comes to rest up-stage right. The dancers now form a compact group of young trees.

The Third Dance—The Air in Spring

The leaves of the trees wave in the spring breeze. The Bird (Strephon) hops on to the stage from down-stage right. The waving of the tree leaves is subdued. The Bird hops into the cornfield. He pecks at the grain. He hops on. He pecks again. He hops farther. The tree leaves begin a spring dance, which increasingly attracts the Bird's attention, as though his nest and mate were in the trees. He attempts to fly, but as one of his wings is broken, he falls at once to the ground. He is quickly up again and tries to fly once more. He falls again, heaves and so stays still. The shadow of the Hawk (a girl dancer) is thrown on to the stage, growing ever larger as she descends. The Bird hops under the protection of the trees. The Hawk turns back without becoming visible and her shadow diminishes and vanishes.

Once more the tree leaves resume their waving in the spring breeze, and the Bird hops out again after the grain. Once more he tries to carry grain into the trees, but when he flies, he falls again. The shadow of the Hawk descending is again projected on the stage, growing ever larger. The Bird with difficulty reaches the shelter of the trees. The Hawk appears and seems to hover on the cornice of the temple just long enough for the audience to see that it is a girl dancer with a bird mask and huge wings. She appears to fly away, her shadow diminishing again to nothing.

The tree leaves resume their waving for the third time. The Bird hurries out to peck the grain in such a frenzy that he pays no attention to the tree leaves' spring dance. However, he makes one last attempt to fly, but falls utterly exhausted. He does not move when the Hawk descends.

The stage darkens nearly to black-out.

Bella, who, with Jack, has been watching this dance with increasing fascination and horror, screams, not knowing if what she sees is real or her own dreams.

Strephon and the Dancers vanish.

Bella	Ah! They'll kill him! *(Clinging to Jack)*

                   Take me away.   Take me away.

                   I can't bear it.

                   (On the verge of hysterics she buries her head in his arms)
                   (The stage darkness lifts in a dazzle of sunlight. The dancers having returned whence they came, the stage looks exactly the same as at the beginning of the Act.)

Jack   There, Bella, steady, steady.
                   It's all right.   I'm here.
                   They've gone now anyway.
                   I wonder who they were.

Bella (half crying)
                   I don't care who they were.
                   It's uncanny and unnatural.
                   I'm sure they meant to kill him.

Jack   Nonsense, Bella, that was only play.
                   You're still a-tremble.
                   I've never known you so upset.
                   You're always sure and strong.

Bella (lifting her head) (sadly)
                   I wasn't born for all these mysteries.
                        (She looks over Jack's shoulder.)
                     (with returning gaiety)
                   Yes, they've gone.

Jack   That's the Bella that I know.
                   That's the voice I'm used to.
                   Let's go together now and find our friends.

Bella   First let me look then in my glass.
                       (She takes it from her pocket or her bag
                          and looks at herself in it.)
                   Oh—my face, my nose, my hair!
                   Hold the glass now, then you'll see
                   How the real Bella's made.

                   They say a woman's glory is her hair.
                   (But only when it's properly displayed!)

Is it tangled?
Then we comb it,
Some to this side,
Some to that.
After, plait the strands together,
(Many a man's been caught for good,
Caught for good in a girl's hair)
Weave the strands together till we
Can with skilful nimble fingers curl them
Up and pin them alluringly round the head.

Turn the glass a little, Jack, the way I need it.

They say a woman's fortune is her face.
(But only if it's given proper care!)
Is it pallid?
Then we paint it,
Some on this cheek,
Some on that.
After rouge the lips with carmine,
                    (*She hums the tune as she paints her lips*)
Line the lips with carmine till we
Can with deftly subtle touches of the powder—
Puff, finish the enchantingly attractive face.

Take a new look at me!
                    (*She turns herself round and Jack admires her*)
You see I'm quite myself again,
Neat and ready to rejoin King Fisher.

Jack (*recoiling*)   King Fisher?

Bella   Oh, yes.   He's summoned both of us.
                You've another role to play.

Jack   Another role to play?   For him?
                What does King Fisher matter now?

Bella   Jack, dear, our love has spoken.
                Our home is sure.
                I'll leave King Fisher at the proper time.
                Today he's still my master,
                And worth our while to suffer.

Jack (*recoiling further*)
>Now I have strange misgivings,
>Unfriendly fancies and forebodings . . .

Bella Don't *you* go silly now.
>Our world is fact not fancy,
>And it's a fact that if you want to keep me
>Catch me if you can, if you can.   (*She runs off L.*)

Jack (*running after her*)
>Bella, Bella . . .

Post-Scene.   CHORUS off stage
(*The Chorus pass behind the hill, returning
from right to left.   The stage remains empty.*)

Chorus (*off stage*)

>In the summer season on the longest day of all
>We wander through the woods where the cunning
>>cuckoos call,
>Crying as they're flying, and this is what they say:
>She must leap and he must fall
>When the bright sun shines on midsummer day.

(*The singing dies away in the distance.
The presences are still.*)

CURTAIN

ACT THREE

(*Evening and Night*)

(*The scene has taken the necessary turn back to the L. from what it was in Act II, so that it is now the same as in Act I. That is, the temple is once again back centre, the stone staircase to the R., the gates and the cave to the L., and the steps leading from the upper to the lower stage in the appropriate place. When the curtain rises, the larger portion of the Chorus is singing and drinking after a meal on the L. of the stage. But it is not clear at first glance what object they are surrounding or what they are laughing at.*)

Scene 1.   CHORUS

Chorus   O-hay! O-hay!
At sundown
Celebrate the day's end
With bread, the fishes and the wine. (*They laugh.*)

(*On the R. of the stage a small group is dancing to the sound of a fiddle. There is a fresh outburst from the group drinking.*)

Chorus   O-hay! O-hay!
At sundown
Celebrate the day's end
With bread, the fishes and the wine.
(*They laugh. The group spreads out and it becomes possible to see that they have given so much wine to one man that he is on the way to being tipsy.*)
Bread and fishes are the food
And wine the drink of men and gods.
And man is a god (so he thinks)
When he's drunk too much!

(*They laugh heartily. The half-tipsy man lurches towards the group that's dancing.*)

Half-Tipsy Man   Shall I dance you a fandango
Boston, rumba or a tango?
I can step as light as any
Of you dainty dancers—

A Dancing Man   Mind out, you fool,
Look where you're going.
Are you blind, are you drunk?
(*The tipsy man gets caught up in the dance. There is general laughter and the dance is given up. Everyone sings.*)

Chorus	For bread
	(When the yellow corn's been ground)
	       is but plain
	And fish
	(When the nets return from the blue sea)
	      but homely fare.
	But wine's pressed out from the ripened grape
	In a red, rich juice for our delight,
	For our delight (or our damnation)
	When the midsummer sun goes down,
	Down the long tunnel to the east
	And the moon at the full, the White Goddess,
	      starts
	Her air-borne journey to the west at night.

Girls	What will the night hold for us?
Men	Her night or his night? King Fisher's summoned us tonight.
Girls	What does the Goddess ask or bring But two things: love or death?
Men	Surely King Fisher did not summon us for love?
Girls	Has he then summoned us for death?

Scene 2.   KING FISHER, BELLA, CHORUS

(King Fisher enters up-stage quickly, with Bella, who carries a belt and holster.)

King Fisher No!   King Fisher summons you for Victory!
            (to Bella)
            Hang the holster on that tree in case of need.
            (to the world at large)
            These Ancients think that they're alone
            In having access to the other world.
            But that's not so.
            I'll show them.   I'll out-magic them.
            I've called my private clairvoyante
            And she'll unravel all their mysteries.
            (turning to the Chorus and striking an attitude)
            Go down and meet Madame Sosostris,
            Greet her with song and lead her
            Up with honours suited to a queen.

Chorus   O-hay!   O-hay!   King Fisher, yes.
            (mimicking King Fisher's attitude)
            We'll go to meet Madame Sosostris,
            Greet her with song and lead her
            Up with honours suited to a queen.
            O-hay!   O-hay!

(They stop attitudinising and go out laughing.)

Scene 3. KING FISHER, BELLA, ANCIENTS

King Fisher Now, Bella, call the Ancients.

Bella Surely you're not wanting them again

King Fisher Indeed, why not?
Please ring at once.

> (*Bella, with less assurance than in the morning, does so.
> The doors of the temple open and the Ancients appear.*)

She-Ancient What is the matter now?

Bella King Fisher wants to speak with you.

She-Ancient If that is so, we're all attention.

King Fisher You two thought to have the better of me
Catching my daughter in your trap like that.
I'm not the man to fall so easily.
I've sent for one who'll see through all your schemes
To hold my daughter from her home.

He-Ancient She is in bondage to her fate, not us.
King Fisher Read me no riddles for I'm in earnest.
Since you are obdurate
Receive my challenge
To a contest between power and power.
The prize is worthy.   It's my daughter.
Defend yourselves!
For conjure what spirits that you may,
Sosostris will outwit you
Though the means be death.

He-Ancient Truly his pride is riding a high
Mare intent to throw him for a fall.

She-Ancient Truly the lure of fruit that hangs
Forbidden draws him blinded to his fate.

Bella (*aside*) Truly I wish that Jack at last
Were here to pour an oil upon this fume.

King Fisher (*aside*)
>Truly they know they're cornered and have lost
>The game before the starting whistle's blown.

He-Ancient (*coming down towards King Fisher*)
>King Fisher, I must give you warning.
>You meddle with powers you cannot gauge,
>Courting a risk you do not understand.
>Should you persist, there's mortal danger
>To your person, and I tell you now:
>Withdraw your challenge while you may.

King Fisher (*histrionically*)
>And even if there's danger to my person,
>What matters that before my daughter's danger?
>And should I further fall and go to ground
>Before the violence of a stronger power,
>Is that no honourable role to play?

She-Ancient He shows a certain courage of his own.

King Fisher That may be so.
>But the point at issue:
>Do you accept my challenge?

He-Ancient Lifted to such lofty heights, I do.

Scene 4. KING FISHER, BELLA, ANCIENTS, CHORUS, JACK

Chorus (*returning from their mission*)
> O-hay! O-hay!

Men
> See! where
> We carry on our mighty shoulder
> The Sphinx and the Sibyl rolled in one.
> *(They enter carrying in procession a figure as though enthroned, dressed in a green cloak and conical hat, masked, or holding a crystal bowl in front of its face. Behind the figure as it comes down centre, members of the Chorus raise flags and banners [or branches] so that temporarily the rest of the stage behind them is out of sight of the audience.)*

Men
> Make way before us!

Girls
> Way before them—

Men
> Kneel before us!

Girls
> Kneel before them—

Chorus, Both Men and Girls   See! where
> We/They carry on our/their mighty shoulder
> The Sphinx and the Sybil rolled in one.
> Behold the Oracle!
> *(The extempore throne is set down and at the same time Bella pushes her way through the crowd to see what is happening. On recognising the cloaked figure preparing to unmask or lower the bowl from before its face, she runs to it, and Jack, for it is now seen to be he, rises to embrace her.)*

Chorus
> Jack!
> What a trick! What a fraud!
> Unscrupulous piece of conjuring!
> You're a technician
> Not a magician.
> Jack of all trades
> Jack of all trades
> What's your role now?
> You in that queer cloak and comic hat
> What's your role now?

Girls
> Dabbling in the magic art *(They all point at Jack.)*

All
> The Sorcerer's Apprentice! *(They all laugh.)*
> *(A gong sounds. In a single movement the flags and banners or branches] are lowered and disappear and the Chorus parts in two. In the centre, just below the steps that lead from the upper to the lower stage, therefore almost in a line with the gates and the staircase, is a huge contraption of black veils of roughly human shape, though much more than life-size.)*

Scene 5. KING FISHER, BELLA, JACK, ANCIENTS, SOSOSTRIS

Chorus (*awed at last*)   Sosostris!
          (*Jack places the crystal bowl beside her*)
King Fisher (*placing himself almost reverentially beside or in front of Sosostris, and speaking almost as if he identified himself with her*)
          I needn't tell Madame Sosostris
          All the story, for she reads
          The past and future like a book.
          My only child and daughter Jenifer's
          Been kidnapped by these wicked people,
          Locked away behind those gates.
          They, past masters of prevarication,
          Deny they hold her.   But they do.
          I failed to make my way by force,
          For they can call upon unnatural power.
                    (*addressing Sosostris directly*)
          Therefore I call on you
          To use your visionary powers
          To see my daughter where she is,
          That I, sustained by your device,
          May go to succour her and set her free.
          You have no cause to fear their force.
          I have no moral need to blench.
          A father may protect his child.
          Begin the contest!
          Examine first the pictures in the bowl
          That I may see, find, speak with Jenifer.
                    (*He moves aside.*)

Chorus   Is there a woman under the black robe?
          Will the voice that answers be a god's?
                    (*Sosostris' veils begin to wave.*)
          Look!   The veils lift on the evening breeze.

Sosostris (*in a deep, slow voice*)
          Who hopes to conjure with the world of dreams,
          Waking to life my visionary powers,
          He draws inexorably out from the vast
          Lottery a dream to dream himself.

The illusion that you practise power is delusion.
(*with gradually rising passion*)
I alone cannot consult myself
I alone draw out no dream
To dream myself awake.
I dream the shadows that you cast.
I am a medium, not an end.
(*crying out*)

O my forgotten and forbidden womanhood!
Must I drink again the potion that dissolves you?
O bitterness, O bitterness of a Pythia's fate!
O body swollen to a monstrous birth!
O horror, horror of transcendent sight!
O tongue taught by a god to cry:
" I am what has been, is and shall be,
No mortal ever lifted my garment."
(*calm and with authority*)

You who consult me
Should never doubt me
Clean let the heart be
Of each seeker.

Truth shall shine through me
Once more endue me
Humble yourselves now
I speak as a seer.
(*in an altered voice*)

Acolyte, Acolyte,
Lift up the bowl that I may look.
(*Jack holds up the bowl before Sosostris. She broods over it.*)
I see a meadow, fragrant with flowers,
and some-one walking there—a girl.

King Fisher (*excited*)   Jenifer!

Sosostris   Fragrant as a flower herself,
She opens her body to the sun.

King Fisher My child, alone and safe.

Sosostris   Oh! but now a lion—
A winged and royal lion—
Enters the flowered field,
Moving with majesty towards the girl.

King Fisher   Then there's danger.
We must warn her.
This is fearful, to be so near and far.

Sosostris   The lion has reached the osier bed
Where she has gone to lie at length.

King Fisher (*covering his eyes*)   O horrible!

Sosostris   As the beast rears rampant
Now I see the face is human
And the wings are arms,
Strong sheltering arms of a manly youth—

King Fisher   Mark!

Sosostris   The glorious lion of love
With symbol erect he . . .

King Fisher (*rushing forward and forcing Jack to lower the bowl*)
No! It's all a hoax, a sham,
A cheat fetched out to frighten me.
Your bowl's a useless and disgusting trick.
              (*snatching the bowl from Jack*)
See, then, what happens to a lie!
        (*He throws the bowl into the wings R. A Crash*)

Scene 6.   THE SAME

Chorus (sotto voce)
> She saw what happens in the soul.
> It's ominous how still she is.

King Fisher   And now, Sosostris, speak the truth.

Chorus   Truth is never spoken twice.
> It's ominous how still she is.

King Fisher   Ah!—does the truth then hurt you?
> Are you dumb?

Chorus   Silence is power.
> It's ominous how still she is.

King Fisher   Jack.   Take off the robes.
> Be quick.
> You'll change your part again.
>> (*He gives a sign to Bella, who goes to fetch
>> the belt and holster from the tree.*)
> Here, take this belt and holster,
> Buckle it fast and so prepare
> To do as I'll command you.

Bella (bringing the belt to Jack)
> O Jack, why did I trust myself and not trust you,
> There in the shadow of the wood?

Jack (taking off the robes)
> I can't undo this pin here, Bella.
> You must help me.
>> (*She does so.   The belt is buckled on.
>> They kiss as though goodbye.*)

Chorus   A brutal dress is a tragic mask
> For a fine young man to wear.
>> (*Jack comes to King Fisher.*)

King Fisher   Since Sosostris will not speak
> Then I must speak.
> Since Sosostris will not act
> Then I shall act.
> Jack—unveil her.

Bella (*crying out*) Sacrilege! Impious crime!
I hardly know the words I speak,
But ah, Jack, for our love's sake, now come away.

King Fisher (*shouting*)
This is no time for a whimpering girl.

He-Ancient (*coming downstage with the She-Ancient to the edge of the upper stage*)
But time for a man to choose his fate.

Chorus (*Men*)   —for a man to choose his fate.

She-Ancient   Time for the unborn child to speak.

Chorus (*Girls*)   —for the unborn child to speak.

Bella (*drawing Jack away downstage right*)
Is there not someone waiting to be born,
Some power, some glory, some nativity
Confined to go the way we choose?

Jack   Is there some vision from a world within,
Keener than prudence or our common sense,
Revealed to all men if we choose?

Chorus (*moving nearer to Jack and Bella and leaving King Fisher alone L.*)
Dear Jack and Bella, choose for us,
For now we know that we accept
Whatever fate your choice may bring.

The Ancients (*moving a little further downstage C.*)
Fate and freedom propound a paradox.
Choose your fate but still the god
Speaks through whatever acts ensue.

King Fisher (*going by himself downstage L.*)
How am I bounded by their menial choice?
I have provoked it.   But not to abdicate
By that one jot or tittle of my power.
(*As the ensemble ceases, Bella turns Jack towards the centre.*)

Bella   Ah, speak, Jack!
Our moment's at its height.
(*She leads Jack centre to face King Fisher.*)

Jack   Young though I am,
This is my choice.
I choose to put away disguise.
I choose to strip the veils
Not from Sosostris but myself.
A builder, I, a builder now,
I choose to throw your badges
At your feet.   There!
Take your infernal belt and holster
Back.   I care not what you do.
(turning his back on King Fisher)
Bella, riding on the great wave's crest, I call.

Bella   Jack, before it falls like thunder in the trough,
      I come.

Chorus (*echoing their afternoon song*)
       . . . call
Crying as they're flying and this is what they say:
He must leap and she must fall
When the bright sun shines on midsummer-day.
(Jack and Bella go off R.)

King Fisher (*shouting after them*)
     All right.   The wood's watched.
     I'll deal with you two later.
     Nor can I be baulked by loss of service

Scene 7. ANCIENTS, KING FISHER, CHORUS

(*The Ancients return upstage. King Fisher stoops to pick up the belt and holster, which he buckles on. He turns round to face the Chorus, who are standing between himself and Sosostris. The Chorus draw back reluctantly to give King Fisher access to Sosostris. King Fisher pauses a moment before he lays his hand on the first veil. He begins to unveil her.*)

The Ancients   Pride is virtue in a man of power
                If pride is of the virtue not the power.

Chorus   Look, the sacred veils are flying
                Torn by King Fisher's violent hand.
                Black snow flung up against the moon
                Darkening further the darkest hour.

The Ancients   Pride though where's no reverence
                Finds conclusion in catastrophe.

Chorus   Soon we shall tremble when the heavy
                Womb is rent asunder ruthlessly.
                  (*At the last veil, King Fisher pauses, for something begins
                     to glow beneath. The glowing increases in intensity.*)

The Ancients and the Chorus
                Sosostris said:
                " I am what has been, is and shall be.
                No mortal ever lifted my garment."
                  (*As King Fisher steels himself to seize the last veil,
                   it falls of itself, disclosing an incandescent bud.*)

Chorus   Prepare then, all we mortals, then prepare
                To turn the face before the face.
                (*The stage is now dark. King Fisher draws back as the bud
opens. When the bud is fully open like huge lotus petals on
the stage, there is still a gauze over the inner shrine. The
Chorus turn away a the gauze falls before the radiant
trans-figuration,* in reds and gold, of Mark and Jenifer
posed in mutual contemplation. †The open petals of the bud
form a circle on the ground. Sosostris has vanished.*)

---

* In Indian mythology, Mark and Jenifer would be transfigured as Shiva-Shakti (Shiva and Parvati). All their gestures and poses are hieratic.

† The outside of Jenifer's right leg is resting on the inside of Mark's left thigh, as they are seated facing the audience, but with their heads turned to each other.

King Fisher (*going downstage*)
    Oh, oh—I'm blinded by the sight.
    But force myself to look.

Chorus   Turn the face before the face.

King Fisher It's Jenifer, my daughter.
    Mark, prepare to die.

Chorus   Turn the face before the face.

King Fisher (*taking the pistol from the holster*)
    This then is victory.
    Jenifer, I free you.

Chorus   Weep, weep for the impious act.
    (*He aims at Mark. Mark and Jenifer turn their faces
    towards him in a gesture of power. King Fisher clutches his
    heart, trembles, and falls to the ground.*)

Scene 8.   ANCIENTS, CHORUS,
later STREPHON, DANCERS

(The men go downstage to King Fisher's body)

A man   King Fisher's dead.

A girl   *(The girls recoil together.)*
        How horrible!
          (Mark and Jenifer assume a pose of compassion.)

He-Ancient (coming down the steps on to the lower stage)
        (to the men)
        Pride has brought him to the ground.
        Carry the King to his grave.
          *(The men lift up the body and slowly carry it upstage
           and into the temple, whose doors open for them.)*

Men (repeatedly)
        Lift him now up with our powerful arms
        Letting our tread compose his requiem.

He-Ancient (to the girls)
        Gather the veils to make him a shroud.
        (The girls collect the veils and shroud the body with them)

Girls (repeatedly)
        Mourn not the fall of a man that goes down
        Leaving the room for someone beautiful.

She-Ancient (coming to the footlights and addressing the audience)
        Blessed the dead!
        For which of you do minister with love
        To the dying under the broken house?
        Blessed the dead! *(She leaves the centre of the stage)*

(Strephon comes out of the temple with the dancers, descending on to the lower stage, the men of the Chorus return behind them. The men of the Chorus remain on the upper stage where the girls of the Chorus are already, while Strephon and another dancer come down in front of Mark and Jenifer and begin to make ritual fire. That is, Strephon twirls a pointed stick within a wooden block, which the other dancer holds before him. With the twirling the stick begins to get hot. As the tinder in the block kindles and the stick itself begins to glow, other dancers fan or blow upon the sparks until at last the stick catches fire and after a while Strephon is able to hold the freely burning stick, clear above his head.)

The Fourth Dance,—Fire in Summer

(Mark and Jenifer have relaxed their compassionate pose and assume one of increasing vigour and ecstasy.)

Chorus	Fire! Fire! St. John's Fire In the desert in the night. Fire! Fire! Fire in summer.

(In the first part of the Fire Dance Strephon dances with the lighted stick, while the other dancers force him back towards the transfiguration of Mark and Jenifer until at last he falls at their feet in the pose of a hieratic pedestal. The lighted stick is taken from him and set above and behind the heads of Mark and Jenifer.)

Mark and Jenifer	Sirius rising as the sun's wheel Rolls over at the utter zenith So the dog leaps to the bull Whose blood and sperm are all fertility.

(In the second part of the Fire Dance, the dancers other than Strephon appear by incantatory gestures to cause the lotus petals or other veils to close themselves back over Mark and Jenifer, in such a way that their bodies disappear from sight from the feet upwards. Strephon is also covered by this means. Finally even the heads disappear and only the lighted stick is visible shining above.)

Chorus (on the upper stage, behind the dancers and the transfiguration)
Carnal love through which the race
Of men is everlastingly renewed
Becomes transfigured as divine
Consuming love whose fires shine
From God's perpetually revealed face.
Wonder! Praise! Rejoice exceedingly!

54

Mark and Jenifer   The world is made by our desire,
Its splendour, yes, even its pain
Becomes transfigured in the bright
Furious incandescent light
Of love's perpetually renewed fire.
Wonder! Praise! Rejoice!

The Ancients (*downstage*)
From heavenly One the Two divide
And Three as Paraclete can make
Symbolic union with the Four,
The messenger, the path, the door
Between the light and dark, the guide.
Wonder! Praise! Rejoice exceedingly!

(When the heads are covered, and the voices have ceased, there is a moment's pause before the lighted stick is drawn down within the veils. The veiled mass glows from within and breaks into flame.)

Chorus   Fire! Fire! St. John's Fire.
In the desert in the night.
Fire! Fire! Fire in summer.

Scene 9. Finale. CHORUS, later MARK, JENIFER

(When the flames and ensuing smoke have died down, the stage is very dark, except for moonlight on the white stone of the temple. Strephon, Mark, Jenifer, the Ancients and the Dancers have all vanished.)

Chorus (*once more downstage*) (*sotto voce*)

Even in a summer night
There comes an hour whose cold
Hand fingers the flesh
And chills the hot heart.
For the sun's lost on the night
Journey through the sea and only
Faith that's beyond fear
Trusts tomorrow's morning.

O summer sun
Golden faced
Glorious globe
Make haste,

Make haste
To find the way
In the dark
To another day.

Was it a vision?
Was it a dream?
In the fading moonlight what shall be seen?
(They turn round to look)
Only the temple on the wooded hill,
The gates and the staircase
Cold and still.

But where, where
Are the plighted pair
The midsummer groom
And bride?   Guide
Them safe to our side.

O summer sun
Golden faced
Glorious globe
Make haste,

56

Make haste
To find the way
In the dark
To another day.

(The moonlight has faded out and the stage is quite dark. As they remain silent for a while, the birds begin singing before dawn. The stage light returns much as at the beginning of Act I. When it is light enough it will be seen that the temple and the sanctuary of buildings have disappeared once more in the morning mist. The voices of Mark and Jenifer are heard calling offstage. They enter at the same time on opposite sides of the stage, both dressed for their wedding.)

Mark *(coming forward to meet Jenifer with youthful warmth, but dignity)*
Jenifer, Jenifer, my darling . . .
After the visionary night
The senses purified
My heart's at rest.

Jenifer   O Mark, truth is assumed
In love so rich
I could love all—
Even my father had he lived.

Mark   Mourn no stubborn father, but receive the ring
Here in this magic wood on this midsummer day.
'All things fall and are built again
And those that build them again are gay.'

Chorus   Let us go down the hill with joy
To the bounteous life of this midsummer day.

All   'All things fall and are built again
And those that build them again are gay.'
(They begin to move off as the sun rises. Their voices disappear in the distance. The stage fills with light. Were the mists to lift again it would be seen that the temple and the sanctuary of buildings were only ruins and stones silhouetted against the clear sky.)

CURTAIN